There are 6 books in all which will take your child from age 3 until Primary One. Younger children won't necessarily understand all the stories. That's fine, they don't have to. Learning to **HOLD HANDS** and **WAIT** are the key points, the rest will come in time.

It's never too early for a child to get into good road safety habits that will last them a lifetime. So make sure they're following the best possible example and Go Safe every time you cross.

KU-478-042

All that's left to say is – enjoy!

The books support Curriculum for Excellence.

Children can follow Ziggy's adventures online at: **www.gosafewithziggy.com**

Shout a big, huge loud-as-you-can hello to Ziggy!

He's come all the way from the planet Cosmos to learn how to Go Safe.

Today Ziggy is going to meet a very special person. Why don't you come too?

Mum, Andrew and Ziggy are taking Maggie to nursery for the first time.

Ziggy wonders if nursery school on this planet is as much fun as nursery school on his planet.

On Ziggy's planet you get to do all sorts of fun things like **sticking** and **playing with gloopy stuff**.

And if you're really good the teacher gives you **a big juicy cabbage**.

(But you have to be really, really, **really** good for that.)

Ziggy can't wait to see Maggie's nursery.
He's so excited that he races off ahead
of the others.

'st**op**!'

shouts mum.

'We're **not** allowed to race off,' says Andrew 'because cars sometimes drive on the pavement.'

'**They do?**' asks Ziggy, his eyes widening.

'Yes,' says Andrew, 'when they're going in and out of driveways.'

'Oooh,' says Ziggy, 'what's a driveway?'

Do you know what a driveway is? Can you tell Ziggy?

'I don't like it that cars can
go on pavements,'
says Ziggy stamping his foot.
'I don't want to get squashed
when I'm walking down
the road.'

**'But you weren't
walking were you,
Ziggy?'** Maggie says crossly.
'You were RUNNING!'

'Don't worry, Ziggy,' smiles Andrew.
'You won't get squashed if you hold
hands and walk with Mum.'

Ziggy decides to **hold hands** the rest of the way.

'Nearly there,' says Mum.

'We'll walk up a bit and cross with the lollipop lady.'

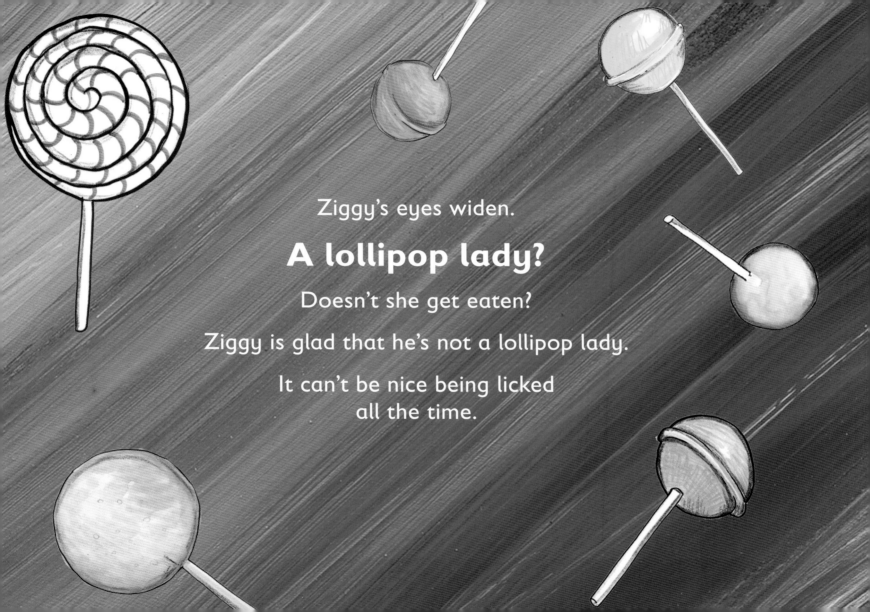

Ziggy's eyes widen.

A lollipop lady?

Doesn't she get eaten?

Ziggy is glad that he's not a lollipop lady.

It can't be nice being licked
all the time.

'Hi Andrew, Hi Maggie,' says a lady with a big pole that says STOP on it.

'Who's this wee man?'

'This is our new friend, Ziggy,' says Andrew proudly. 'He's visiting our planet to learn all about **crossing the road safely.'**

'I'm sure you'll get the hang of it in no-time, Ziggy' smiles the lollipop lady.

'Do you know who I am?'

Ziggy shakes his head.

He's pretty sure he's never seen this lady before.

He wonders if she could be someone who's on the telly.

Silly Ziggy.

Why don't you whisper who she is in Ziggy's ear?

'Ah, you're **the lollipop lady!'** says Ziggy.

(He must have heard you!)

'That's right, Ziggy,' she smiles.

'It's my job to help children cross the road safely. This is my lollipop.'

Ziggy takes a picture of the lollipop. It doesn't look much like any lollipop he's ever seen.

For a start it's much,
much, much bigger.

And it says **STOP** on it.
But there's something about the bright
yellow and red colours that make
it look strangely tasty…

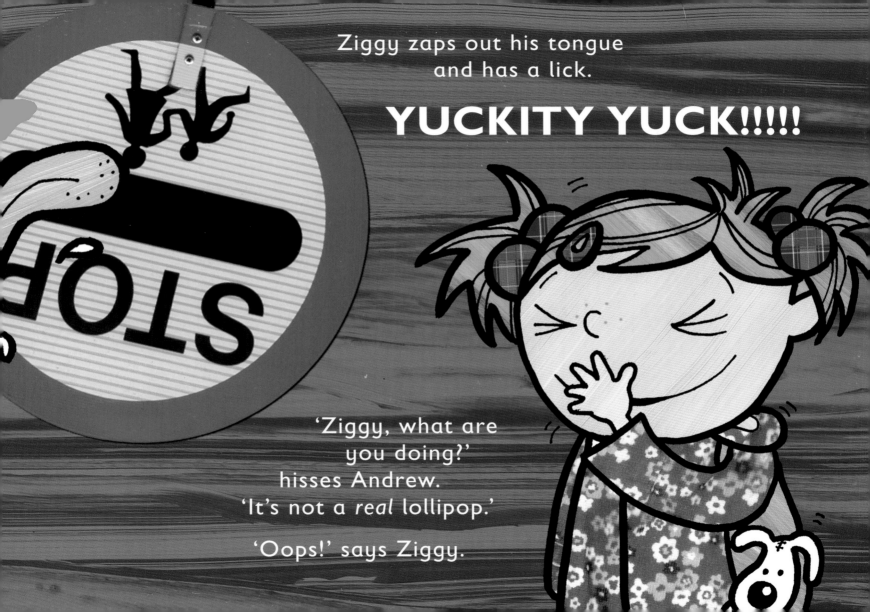

'Now wee Ziggy,'
says the lollipop lady.
**'do you know
what we have to
do before we
cross the road?'**

Ziggy thinks.

He had no idea that you had to do
anything before you crossed the road.

'Um... have breakfast?'
he mumbles.

His Mummy is always telling him
that you can't do anything
without having breakfast.

'We always have to **wait** before we cross the road,' chips-in Maggie. 'I'm a big nursery girl now, so I know LOTS.'

'And we always have to **hold hands,**' adds Andrew. 'That's really important.'

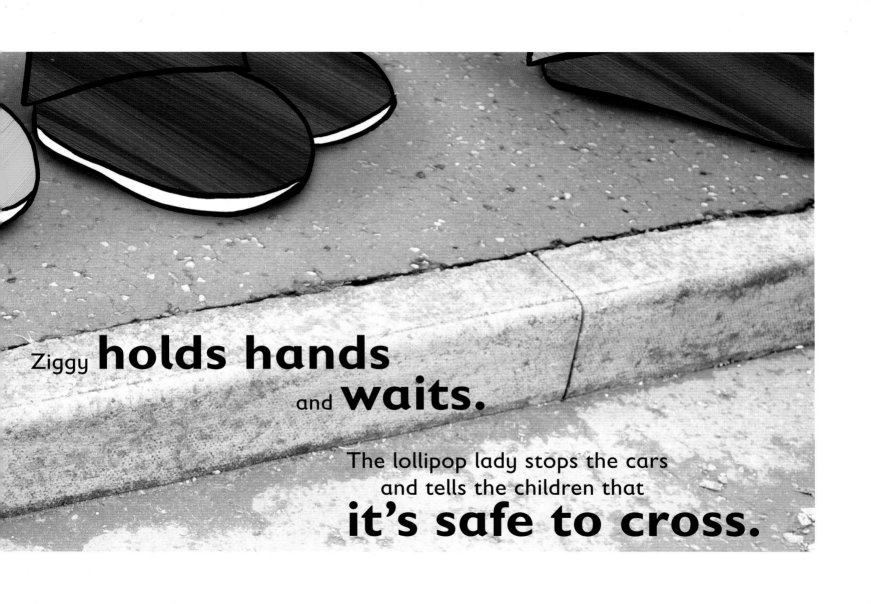

Ziggy **holds hands**
and **waits.**

The lollipop lady stops the cars
and tells the children that
it's safe to cross.

'Here we go,' says Mum.
'**Hold on** everyone
and **keep looking**
and **listening**
for **traffic.**'

Everyone crosses safely
to the other side.

'Zab-a-Ding-a-Doo! Zab-a-Ding-a-Doo!'

squeals Ziggy and gives Maggie
and Andrew a big high five.

'Dinga-Dabba-Poo-ooo!'
squeals Maggie, not getting
it quite right.

'Well done everyone!'
says Mum proudly.

'Does that mean we can have
a treat after school?'
asks Andrew excitedly.

'We'll see,' smiles Mum.

At home time, Andrew races over
to Mum, Maggie and Ziggy.

'Ziggy's got a treat for you' grins Mum.

Can you guess what **treat**
Ziggy chose for Andrew?

A yellow and red **lollipop!**
And what treat did Ziggy choose for himself?

A big juicy **cabbage**, of course.
'The lollipops. on your planet
are **YUCK,'**

Ziggy laughs.

Especially the big ones!'

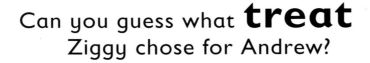

What you should know about crossing the road with pre-school children

Just talking about **stop**, **look** and **listen** isn't enough.

Young children find it difficult to stop and will be too easily distracted to properly look and listen for traffic.

Children aren't ready to cross a road by themselves until they are at least **8 years of age**.

Real learning comes from real experiences.

Every time you cross a road with a young child, the child will learn from **what you do and what you say.**

Every time.

If you take risks when crossing the road, the child with you **won't** learn to Go Safe.